Roasted

Roasted

a cartoon strip about stuff...

Andy Riley

HODDER & STOUGHTON

First published in Great Britain in 2007 by Hodder & Stoughton
A division of Hodder Headline

A Hodder & Stoughton Book

1

A CIP catalogue record for this title is available from the British Library

Hardback ISBN 978 0 340 95326 6

Printed and bound in Italy by Graphicom Srl

Hodder Headline's policy is to use papers that are natural, renewable and recyclable products and made from wood grown in sustainable forests. The logging and manufacturing processes are expected to conform to the environmental regulations of the country of origin.

Hodder & Stoughton Ltd
A division of Hodder Headline
338 Euston Road
London NW1 3BH

With thanks to:

Ian Tucker, Allan Jenkins, Balwant Ahira,
Caroline McGivern and all at the Observer Magazine,
Nick Davies and all at Hodder, Camilla Hornby,
Polly Faber, Kevin Cecil, Robin Riley and Greta Riley

and H.M.Bateman, Peter Bagge and
Kevin Smith for inspiration

Introduction

Their names are Karl, Lottie and Nev, and they work in a coffee shop. That's all you need to know. Actually, you don't really even need to know their names; you just need to recognise the sort of people they are - the care-worn, balding thirty-year-old, keenly aware he's on the final lap of his youth, the girl who frets about everything (but food in particular), and the chirpy big-eyed twat with one of those unfortunate faces that you just want to hit. I've been drawing them in the Observer Magazine for five years as they thrash their way through the nettles of the zeitgeist. Looking over the early ones now, some I could have drawn yesterday, while others, especially ones about iPods and new kinds of phone, are already reading like historical curios. Read them yourself and see how fast civilisation is changing. Sorry we couldn't reprint the two and four page holiday specials here; the only reason is the pages aren't big enough.

I designed the characters in 2002 at a time when I just didn't like drawing noses. I barely have a sense of smell, and if I want to breathe there's always my mouth, so who needs the stupid nostril-riddled bastard? I'm much more of a nasalist now, at least in character design. But you can't suddenly go back and change a cartoon character, can you? It would be like giving Walter the Softie a Hoxton fin. So noseless they'll stay. I was co-writing the sitcom Black Books then, and I think Bernard Black's dress sense rubbed off on Karl, along with some of his poisonous negativity. Lottie is physically based on the actress Sarah Alexander who I know a little bit from Armstrong and Miller days. Or at least Sarah Alexander if she suddenly piled on about three stone. But I kept the face, the hair and especially the cobalt blue eyes, which are normally the very last thing I paint - that's why I forget to do them five percent of the time. An actor we use in Hyperdrive has twice told me how much he has the hots for Lottie. I felt a need to protect her; then I remembered she wasn't real. I do wonder what he does with the OM on a Sunday morning though.

And Nev is just Nev.

(There was an Australian character called Greg but I binned him after two months because I could never figure out how to draw him from more than one angle.)

Anyway, enjoy the strip; one of the very few around that's coloured in using real paints, not Photoshop. I'm 'kicking it old school' and 'keeping it real', you see.

Love

Andy Riley

Roasted
UM...
I'D LIKE, A, UMM, A "SKINNY" ONE, PLEASE
IF YOU WANT SKIMMED MILK ASK FOR A "SKINNY"

A, ERR, AN AMERICANARINO AND COULD IT BE ERR....
"SKINNY?"
IF YOU WANT SKIMMED MILK ASK FOR A "SKINNY"

...AND DO IT SO IT'S AH, OH, WHATEVER IT IS, A "SKINNY" ONE.
YEAH. "SKINNY."
IF YOU WANT SKIMMED MILK ASK FOR A "SKINNY"

IF YOU WANT SKIMMED MILK ASK FOR A
SKIMMED MILK

Roasted
WELCOME TO THE ODEON FILMLINE! PLEASE SAY THE NAME OF THE ODEON CINEMA YOU ARE CALLING FOR.

UNDERPANTS.

I'M SORRY. I'M UNABLE TO IDENTIFY WHICH CINEMA YOU ARE CALLING FOR.
TK

ONE DAY.

Roasted
WHERE ARE YOU?...
"AT WORK." YEAH. SURE. "AT WORK."

WELL SEND ME A PICTURE MESSAGE THEN!!

HMMM.

GOOD GOD. THAT'S THE FUTURE FOR ALL OF US.
IF ANDRE DOES THAT TO STEFFI, MY FAITH IN CELEBRITY MARRIAGES IS COMPLETELY GONE.
Andy Riley

Roasted
FORGET IT.
ACCEPT YOUR TIME HAS PASSED.
UNDER 25s ONLY.
Andy Riley

Roasted
HELLO-
I THINK I LEFT A LAPTOP HERE. DID YOU FIND IT OR DID ANYONE HAND IT IN OR-
...THIS ONE?

THANKS. OH, GOD, YOU'VE SAVED MY LIFE. THANKS.

I TURNED IT ON TO SEE WHOSE IT WAS.
INTERESTING PICTURES.

Andy Riley
I DIDN'T REALLY TURN IT ON.
I JUST LOVE WATCHING THEIR FACES.

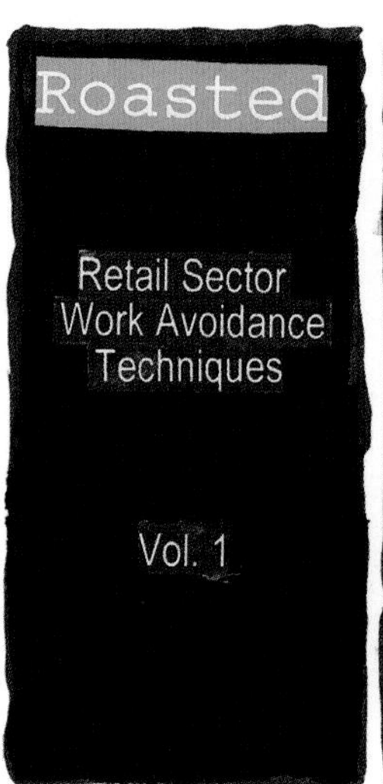
Roasted
Retail Sector
Work Avoidance
Techniques
Vol. 1

1
REFUSAL TO MAKE EYE CONTACT

2
WE'RE JUST WAITING FOR MORE FIVERS.

3
ANECDOTE TOLD IN DOORWAY

3
(CONTD.)
Andy Riley

Roasted
KARL?
SHOULD I CLEAN THIS?
KARL?
KARL, WHERE DO I PUT THIS?
KAA-ARRL.
KARL? DO I ORDER MORE 16 oz CUPS?
KARL. KARL.
KARL.
KARL.
CANED IT
DO NOT WAKE TILL 11 AM

Roasted
LOTTIE.
COULD YOU FIND THE CD WE PUT ON EVERY DECEMBER, PLEASE?

Christmas
CLASSICS

MASH
MASH
MASH

THANK YOU.
COULD YOU PUT IT AWAY NOW PLEASE?
Andy Riley

Roasted
-SO I ANSWERED THE DOOR? AND THERE WAS THIS TAXI? BUT I HADN'T ORDERED ONE?
THAT HAPPENED TO ME ONCE?...

KARL REALISES THAT EVERYONE UNDER 25 NOW ENDS EACH SENTENCE WITH AN UPWARD INFLECTION

KARL THINKS ABOUT CONSCIOUSLY PICKING IT UP AS A YOUTHFUL AFFECTATION

KARL THINKS BETTER OF IT

HE NEVER TELLS ANYONE OF THIS PRIVATE DEFEAT –
I'D LIKE A CAPPUCCINO? TO TAKE AWAY?
BUT NOW, AT LEAST, HE HAS ONE MORE PET RESENTMENT TO COMFORT HIM IN HIS OLD AGE
Andy Riley

Roasted
"Morning After The Work Christmas Party" Special

Andy Riley

Roasted
IT SAYS HERE THAT MY BREAKFAST CEREAL IS THE SECOND MOST UNHEALTHY ONE YOU CAN BUY!

WHICH ONE DO YOU EAT?
"CHOCONUT CHOC FROSTED SUGAR NUT CHOC LOOPS."

THAT'LL BE THE WHEAT IN IT.
THAT'S RIGHT.
AndyRiLey

Roasted
Andy Riley
DO I KNOW YOU?
I'M KARL BANNERMAN.

BETWEEN 1985 AND 1990 YOU MADE MY LIFE A LIVING HELL.

AND NOW YOU PAY!
Y-YOU... NO... PLEASE...
ANYONE YOU'LL GET IN TOUCH WITH THEN?
MAYBE.
IS IT BETTER IF HE DOESN'T BEG?
HMM- NO...
FRIENDS REUNITED

Roasted
OH MY GOD!
I KNOW!
IT'S MY TEXTING HAND!
Andy Riley

Roasted
THANK GOD. LUNCH BREAK.
THERE'S ONLY SO MANY HOURS A DAY YOU CAN SPEND IN A PLACE LIKE THIS.

Andy Riley

Roasted
Andy Riley

*** "WELL, REALLY, IT'S ALL ABOUT OIL" —**

.....THE OFFICIAL CONVERSATIONAL DEFAULT SETTING OF **GULF WAR II**™!!

- EASY TO REMEMBER – EASY TO SAY!
- ROUNDS OFF CONVERSATIONS NICELY – SO PEOPLE WON'T FOLLOW IT WITH DETAILED QUESTIONS! THEY'LL ASSUME YOU UNDERSTAND THE COMPLEX ISSUES!
- YOUNG, SEXY LIBERALS WILL WANT TO KNOW **YOU** BETTER!!

......USE IT!!

Roasted
I SAVED UP AND I BOUGHT IT AND YOU CAN FIT 4000 SONGS ON IT.
4000.
SO WHAT'S WRONG?

I'VE ONLY GOT 51 CDs. THAT'S NOT EVEN A THOUSAND SONGS!
NOT EVEN 25%!!

NOT EVEN....
A QUARTER...
I'LL NEVER FILL IT....
AH.
I-POD INADEQUACY.
YEP.
Andy Riley

Roasted<<<

1989
...WE SHOULD PUT SANCTIONS ON SOUTH AFRICA, DEFINITELY.
IT'S THE ONLY WAY TO GET RID OF APARTHEID! PUT THE PRESSURE ON THE RICH!!
YEAH.
TOTALLY.

2003
...WE SHOULD STOP SANCTIONS ON IRAQ, DEFINITELY.
SANCTIONS DON'T WORK! ALL THEY DO IS HURT THE POOR!
YEAH.
SPOT ON.
****
Andy Riley

DESIGNATED
'PACING UP AND DOWN YAPPING ON YOUR MOBILE'
ROUTE
PLEASE STAY IN LANE
Andy Riley

Roasted
TK
TK
TK
TK

PLEASE TAKE YOUR CARD AND WAIT FOR YOUR MONEY
YOUR ACCOU
BALANCE I

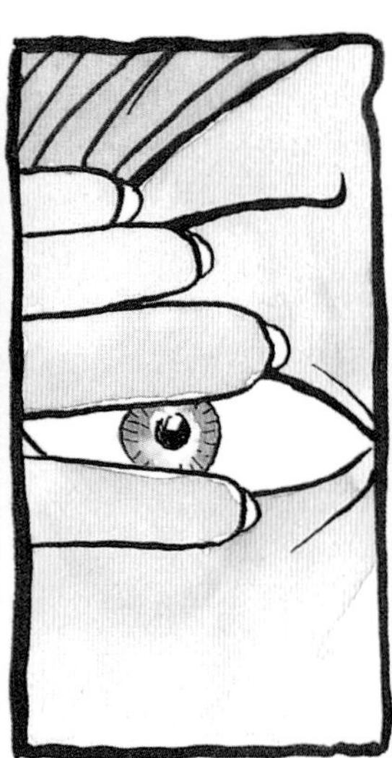

NEVER OPEN THE HAND. NEVER OPEN THE HAND. NEVER OPEN THE HAND.
Andy RiLey

>>>Roasted

THE DAY THEY CHANGED THEM
Huge massive scary warning
You're actually *reading* this
Wow

NOW
Completely invisible
...again
Oh well, it worked for a week
Andy Riley

Roasted
KARL WONDERS WHY THIS GULF WAR BOTHERS HIM LESS THAN THE FIRST ONE

IT'S STILL BRUTAL AND HORRIBLE AND MIGHT ESCALATE AND EVERYTHING...
****

THEN HE REMEMBERS!
HE'S PROBABLY TOO OLD TO BE CALLED UP THIS TIME
****

Epilogue
(UNLESS IT ESCALATES REALLY, REALLY BADLY)
Andy Riley

Roasted
WHAT'S UP?
I NEED DIRECTORY ENQUIRIES.

I DON'T KNOW, DO I RING 11 88 88 OR 118 118 OR DO I KICK IT OLD SCHOOL AND RING 192?

DAMN THEM! I NEVER HAD TO MAKE THIS DECISION BEFORE!!

I DON'T WANT CHOICE! I NEVER WANT CHOICE!
MAKE IT ALL GO AWAY.

>>Roasted
Blue Wine Bottle Paranoia
GREEN GLASS ONLY
CLEAR GLASS ONLY
ALL GREEN WINE BOTTLES NOW TURQUOISE! —SUSPECT SOUGHT
WHO MADE ALL OUR CLEAR BOTTLES BLUISH?
POLICE RELEASE E-FIT
Andy Riley

Roasted
YESTERDAY ME SET THAT ALARM.
EEP EEP

YESTERDAY ME THOUGHT TODAY ME SHOULD GO FOR A RUN BEFORE WORK.
YESTERDAY ME SET THE ALARM WHEN HE GOT BACK FROM THE PUB.
EEP EEP
6:50

WHY COULDN'T YESTERDAY ME GO FOR A RUN? HE MAKES TODAY ME DO EVERYTHING.
I HATE YESTERDAY ME. TODAY ME WANTS HIM TO DIE.
EEP EEP
6:50

EEP EEP
6:51

TOMORROW ME. HE LIKES RUNNING.
IP
Andy RiLey

>>>Roasted<<<
Find Your
Cashpoint Beggar Liberal Embarrassment Rating
How far will you walk to find an unmanned ATM?
0 yards: you're either unashamed of your wealth, or moved enough to give him something. FAIL!
50 yards: more like it, but you probably didn't cross a road.
100 yards +: you're very guilty but will you actually give? Never! Top marks!
PROPER LIBERAL!
Andy Riley

Roasted
Andy Riley
....YEAH, BUT HE'S A PRAT ISN'T HE?
"PRAT?"
WHAT?
NO-ONE SAYS PRAT ANY MORE.
NO. NOT SINCE 1990 AND THE COMPLETE ASCENDANCY OF "TWAT."
TWAT'S HAD IT GOOD FOR A LONG TIME.
THAT'S WHY I'M SWITCHING TO PRAT. IT'S AN 80s RETRO INSULT!!
IT'LL BE HUGE LIKE SCHOOL DISCO OR GTA VICE CITY AND I'M STARTING IT OFF!
THE PRAT REVIVAL. IT CAN'T WORK...
CAN IT?
IT WILL. AND ANYONE WHO DOESN'T THINK SO IS A RIGHT WALLY.
Say
"Prat"
...catch the
80s wave!

>Roasted<
A MYSTERIOUS, YET POWERFUL FORCE PREVENTED THEM FROM ENTERING THE PUB
LUNCH TIME JAZZ
Andy RiLey

Roasted
LOOK AT THEM.
BLOKES IN OPEN TOP CARS DRIVING UP AND DOWN. UP AND DOWN.

THERE'S ABOUT TWO WEEKS OF THE SUMMER IT'S WORTHWHILE HAVING ONE SO THEY HAVE TO DRIVE THEM ROUND ALL DAY.
JUST TO KID THEMSELVES AND THE WORLD IT WAS A GOOD PURCHASE.
Andy RiLey

UP AND DOWN. UP AND DOWN.

BUT I BET YOU' REALLY L
DON'T BE STUPID. IT'S JUNE, I'M A MAN. OF COURSE I'D LIKE ONE.

Roasted
THIS BIG BROTHER'S DEFINITELY NOT AS GOOD AS THE LAST THREE. I'M NOT REALLY WATCHING IT, TO BE HONEST.
MM.

LOOK, I DON'T CARE WHAT ANYONE SAYS. I THINK BIG BROTHER'S BRILLIANT THIS YEAR. YOU SHOULD JUST RELAX, GET INTO IT.
MM.

EH?
I'M TRYING THEM BOTH OUT. SEEING WHICH SOUNDS COOLEST WHEN YOU SAY IT.
Andy Riley

IF THE MATRIX IS REALLY 1000s OF YEARS OLD, DOES IT STAY PERMANENTLY IN THE LATE 20TH / EARLY 21ST CENTURY? SO IN THE MATRIX YOU LIVE THE SAME DAY OR YEAR OVER AND OVER?
THAT WOULD SAVE A LOT OF MEMORY SPACE SO, FROM THE POINT OF VIEW OF THE COMPUTERS, THAT MAKES A LOT OF SENSE.

OKAY, WHAT ABOUT THIS. IF ZION HAS RESTARTED SIX TIMES, WHY DON'T THE 23 SELECTED HUMANS TELL THEIR DESCENDANTS ABOUT THE PREVIOUS ZIONS? IT'S NOT IN THEIR INTEREST TO COVER UP THE TRUTH!
SEE WHAT I MEAN?

AH! AH! THEN, RIGHT, THERE'S THAT BIT WHERE NEO STOPS THE ROBOTS OUTSIDE THE MATRIX. HOW COULD HE DO THAT - UNLESS THE 'REAL WORLD' IS JUST ANOTHER MATRIX? A MATRIX OUTSIDE A MATRIX!!
A KIND OF "ÜBER-MATRIX!!

THAT'S WHAT SCIENCE FICTION DOES TO PEOPLE.
GOD. TERMINATOR 3 COMES OUT SOON.
WHAT'S THE CORRECT PLURAL FOR MATRIX FILMS? MATRIXES OR MATRICES?
Andy Riley

Roasted
RIN
DID YOU KNOW, 80% OF COMMUNICATION IS NON-VERBAL?

RINKS
OKAY THEN. FIND A WAY OF TELLING ME THAT FACT NON-VERBALLY.

RINKS

AH.
CASE CLOSED!
Andy Riley

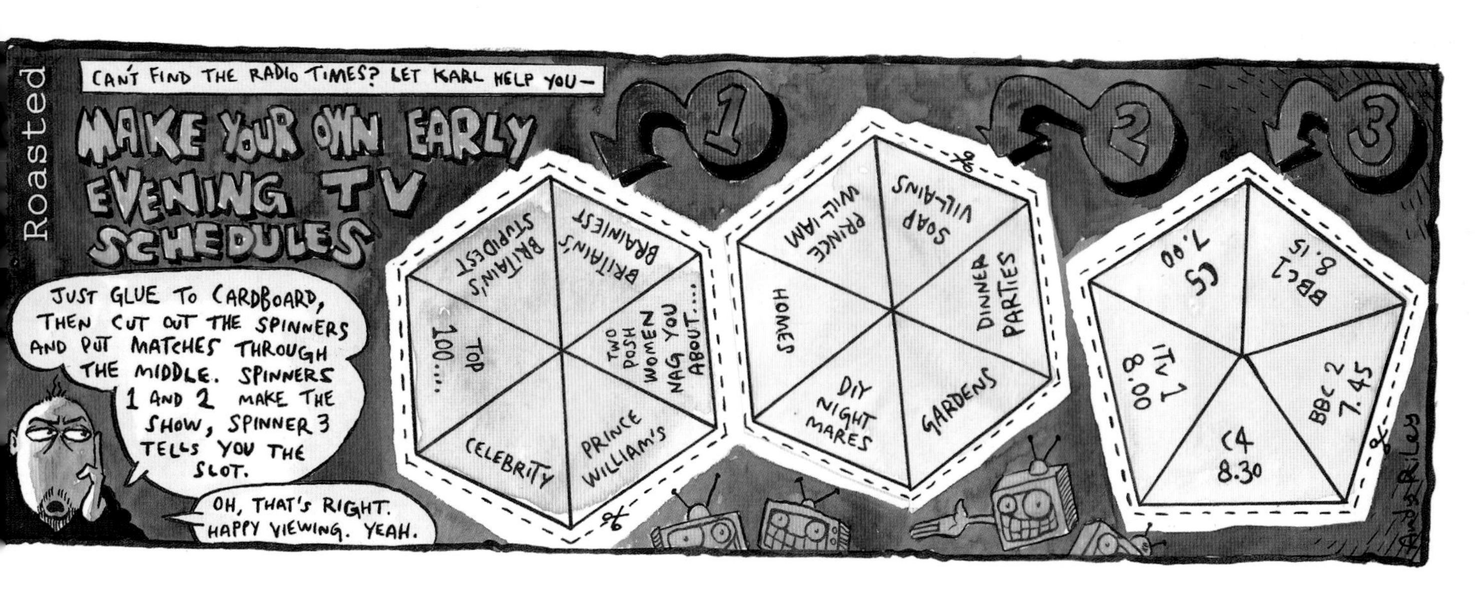
Roasted
CAN'T FIND THE RADIO TIMES? LET KARL HELP YOU—
MAKE YOUR OWN EARLY EVENING TV SCHEDULES
JUST GLUE TO CARDBOARD, THEN CUT OUT THE SPINNERS AND PUT MATCHES THROUGH THE MIDDLE. SPINNERS 1 AND 2 MAKE THE SHOW, SPINNER 3 TELLS YOU THE SLOT.
OH, THAT'S RIGHT. HAPPY VIEWING. YEAH.
1
2
3
BRITAIN'S STUPIDEST
BRITAIN'S BRAINIEST
TWO POSH WOMEN NAG YOU ABOUT....
PRINCE WILLIAM'S
CELEBRITY
TOP 100....
SOAP VILL-AINS
PRINCE WILL-IAM
DINNER PARTIES
GARDENS
DIY NIGHT MARES
HOMES
BBC 1 8.15
BBC 2 7.45
C4 8.30
ITV 1 8.00
C5 7.00
Andy Riley

Roasted
....SO I SENT THE E-MAIL, AND THEY CLEANED OUT MY ACCOUNT!!
THEY NEVER EVEN SENT THE VIAGRA!!

WELL....
YOU WON'T BE DOING THAT AGAIN SOON.
NO WAY! HA HA!!

I SUPPOSE IT'S GOOD YOU'RE LAUGHING ABOUT IT.
OH, I CAN AFFORD TO. BLOKE IN NIGERIA'S SENDING ME TWO MILLION QUID NEXT WEEK.
NICE.

Roasted
FIREMEN.
Andy Riley

Roasted
(OR IF
THERE'S A
QUEUE,
OBVIOUSLY)

WET FLOOR
ABOUT 2 HOURS
AGO, NOW BONE
DRY BUT STAFF
TOO LAZY TO
REMOVE SIGN

THIEVES OPERATING
PLEASE PLACE BAGS ON
HOOKS UNDERNEATH
TABLES, SLIGHTLY
OUT OF YOUR LINE
OF SIGHT SO YOU
FORGET THEM WHEN
YOU LEAVE

Roasted
WEEEEYYY!! I WENT TO BARCELONA FOR THE WEEKEND!
WEEYYY!

WHAT DID THE TICKETS COST?
TWELVE POUNDS?
TWELVE POUNDS!!
TWELVE POUNDS!

WHAT DID YOU SPEND WHEN YOU GOT THERE?
SIX HUNDRED POUNDS.

WEEEYYYYYY!!
Andy Riley

Roasted
Andy Riley
IN THE FIRST FILM WE LEARN THAT METAL CAN ONLY BE SENT BACK IN TIME IF IT'S SURROUNDED BY LIVING TISSUE. BUT IN FILMS 2 AND 3, THEY SEND BACK PURELY METAL TERMINATORS.
HOW?

THE MILITARY HAVE BUILT 1ST GENERATION TERMINATORS BY THE TIME OF THE NUCLEAR WAR, BUT IF THE WAR WIPES OUT HUMAN SOCIETY, HOW CAN THE MACHINES BUILD ANY MORE TERMINATORS? – THEY'D NEED ROBOT MINERS FOR THE STEEL AND THE MILITARY WOULDN'T HAVE BUILT THOSE!! WOULD THEY?

ALSO –
WOULDN'T THE ELECTRO-MAGNETIC PULSES OF ALL THOSE EXPLOSIONS ACTUALLY DESTROY THE COMPUTERS AS WELL AS THE HUMANS?
– AND WHY DIDN'T THE MACHINES SEND ALL 3 BAD TERMINATORS TO THE SAME MOMENT IN TIME? SARAH CONNOR AND JOHN CONNOR COULD NEVER SURVIVE A COMBINED ATTACK.

IT'S ME.
CHANGE OF PLAN. HOW ABOUT PIRATES OF THE CARIBBEAN?

Roasted
BREAD.

WHEAT.

CARBOHYDRATE.

STOP IT. YOU KNOW I LIKE IT WHEN YOU TALK DIRTY.
"EAT ME! I'M A LITTLE MUFFIN! EAT ME!!"
Andy Riley

Roasted
SELF-HELP BOOKS

SELF-
CAN I HELP YOU?
Andy Riley

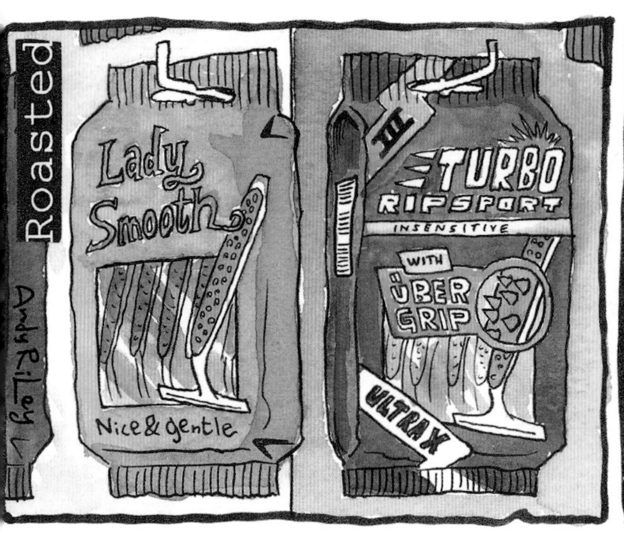
Roasted
Andy Riley
Lady Smooth
Nice & gentle
III
TURBO
RIPSPORT
INSENSITIVE
WITH
ÜBER GRIP
ULTRA X

DON'T BE CONNED. IGNORE THE PACKAGING.
IT'S THE SAME PRODUCT. IT'S THE SAME RAZOR.

THEY WANT YOU TO BUY THE BLUE ONE. SHOW YOU HAVE FREE WILL! BUY THE PINK ONE!! THE PINK ONE!!

YEAH, RIGHT.

Roasted
JOINING MENSA
FOR DUMMIES
Andy Riley

Roasted
Andy Riley
...AND THERE'S THE CAMERA AT THE TOP THERE.
WHAT'S THE RESOLUTION?

ONE POINT FIVE MILLION.
OH.
MINE'S THREE POINT ONE.
DKK!!

PIXEL ENVY

Roasted
YOU CAME FOR A FLASH MOB, DIDN'T YOU?
SPOSE...
NO-ONE ELSE CAME, DID THEY?
UMM.... ...NO.
FFEE HOLE

MOMENTS OF TIME YOU NEVER RECALL LATER ON, No.15:
EMINEM
THE SECONDS YOU SPEND STARING AT LOOSE AA BATTERIES, AS IF YOU CAN TELL THE GOOD ONES FROM THE DEAD ONES JUST BY LOOKING
Andy Riley

Roasted

NEED TO BUY A PRESENT FOR SOMEONE?
STUCK FOR IDEAS?

THEN GO TO A STUPID SHOP AND BUY SOME BIG CANDLES!
CANDLES ARE —...
> NOT TOO DEAR!
> IMPOSSIBLE FOR PEOPLE TO CLAIM THAT THEY'LL NEVER USE!
> EVEN THOUGH THEY NEVER WILL!

IT'S THE GIFT THAT SAYS: "I HAVE ABSOLUTELY NO IDEA WHAT TO BUY YOU. WE'RE MEANT TO BE CLOSE BUT I HAVE NO IDEA AT ALL. WE ARE DRIFTING APART, SLOWLY, STEADILY, LIKE RUDDERLESS BOATS BORNE BY THE EBB TIDE."
3 YEAR'S TIME - YOU WON'T NEED TO BUY THEM ANY PRESENT!

Roasted
...SO YOU'RE OVER HIM THEN, PRETTY MUCH.
OH, DEFINITELY.

THESE DAYS I HARDLY EVER THINK ABOUT COLLECTING ALL MY TEARS IN THE FREEZER AND MAKING THEM INTO AN ICICLE WHICH I'LL USE TO PIERCE HIS SO-CALLED HEART.
Andy Riley

MOMENTS OF YOUR LIFE YOU CAN NEVER RECALL LATER ON, NO. 29:
HMM....
3 LOAVES OF WHITE BREAD... DRINKING STRAWS... CIDER....
THE SEVEN SECONDS YOU SPEND LOOKING AT THE NEXT PERSON'S SHOPPING AT THE SUPERMARKET, FROM WHICH YOU ATTEMPT TO DEDUCE THAT PERSON'S LIFESTYLE, HABITS, PAST, & LOVE LIFE

Roasted
NOD
NOD
NOD
NOD

KARL, HAVE YOU SEEN THE
SHUSH!! I'M TRYING TO LIKE DIZZEE RASCAL.
IT'S VERY HARD. IT TAKES ALL MY CONCENTRATION.

HUH. SEE WHAT YOU'VE DONE?
IT SOUNDS LIKE A RACKET AGAIN.
HOURS, THAT TOOK ME!

Roasted
I DON'T CARE IF IT WAS JUST MY DREAM.
YOU WERE STILL HORRIBLE TO ME IN IT AND I WANT TO KNOW WHY!

Roasted
HMMM. THIS'LL DO AS A CHRISTMAS PRESENT FOR A FEW PEOPLE.
I BET I'VE SEEN MOST OF THE EPISODES TWICE THOUGH. HOPEFULLY NO-ONE'LL BUY IT FOR ME.
the office series 2 DVD
Andy Riley
boxing day
...IT SAYS "WHAT ARE YOUR STRENGTHS," AND YOU PUT, "ACCOUNTS."

Roasted
moments of realisation

I'LL NEVER BE THE NEW JAMES BOND.

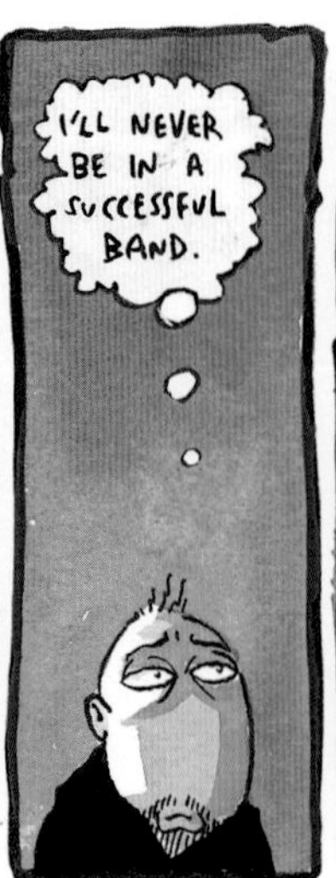
I'LL NEVER BE IN A SUCCESSFUL BAND.

I'LL NEVER SUDDENLY DISCOVER I'M A NATURAL ENTREPRENEUR AND MAKE MILLIONS IN THREE YEARS.

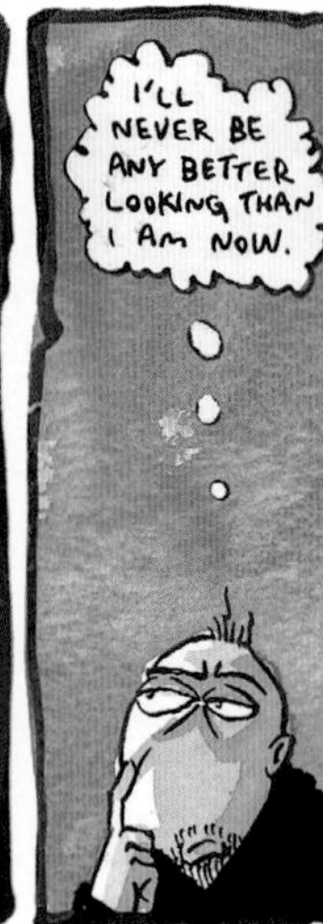
I'LL NEVER BE ANY BETTER LOOKING THAN I AM NOW.

I'LL NEVER AFFORD A REALLY COOL CAR UNTIL I'M THAT OLD IT'LL MAKE ME SEEM LIKE I'M HAVING A MID-LIFE CRISIS.

glue on a photo of
yourself, write on th
dotted lines and hav
your own moment o
realisation!
Andy Riley

Roasted
HMMMM.
A BAD FACE DAY.
Andy Riley

Roasted
KARL. IS RUGBY UNFASHIONABLE AGAIN?
ANY DAY NOW.
THANK GOD.
Latte
Mocha
Tea
Andy Riley

I'M EATING CHIPS.
BUT I'VE JUST BEEN TO THE GYM.
SO IT'S ALL OKAY.
ANYTHING YOU EAT JUST AFTER THE GYM HAS NO CALORIES.
IT'S MAGIC!!
FISH BAR
Andy Riley

Roasted

We tried to deliver an item of mail but you were out. Please collect it from your local Royal Mail Delivery Office:
ADDRESS:
UNIT 3,
INDUSTRIAL ESTATE YOU'VE NEVER HEARD OF,
FURTHER AWAY THAN SATURN'S OUTERMOST MOON,
W39 QZK
HOURS, MON - FRI: DURING NORMAL WORKING HOURS SO YOU, LIKE MOST OTHER PEOPLE, CAN'T PICK IT UP AT ALL IN THE WEEK.
SATURDAY: FOR ABOUT TWO MINUTES, IN THE HOUR BEFORE SUNRISE.
PLEASE BRING THIS CARD AND 23 PROOFS OF IDENTITY INCLUDING PASSPORT, SCHOOL REPORTS, DNA PROFILE, RETINA SCAN, KGB DOSSIER, THUMB AND KNEE PRINTS, TWO

Andy Riley

Roasted
SMALL DISAPPOINTMENTS, NUMBER 9 :
PUTTING YOUR NAME INTO GOOGLE AND FINDING THE PERSONAL WEBSITES OF 22 MORE SUCCESSFUL VERSIONS OF YOU
Andy Riley

Roasted
Andy Riley
DE-CLUTTERING
DE-CLUTTER NOW!!
DE-CLUTTER
END YOUR CLUTTER
DE-CLUTTER YOUR LIFE!
DE-CLUTTER + STAY THAT WAY
HOW TO DE-CLUTTER
DE-CLUTTER
HOW TO BEAT CLUTTER
HOW TO STAY DE-CLUTTERED
DE-CLUTTER
DE-CLUTTER

Roasted
KARL. EX-EMPLOYEE SHOWING OFF NEW BABY ALERT.
OOO!!
WE WON'T ALL HAVE TO HOLD IT AND SAY SOMETHING, WILL WE?
OOO!!

... AND THIS IS UNCLE KARL....

HE LOOKS EXACTLY LIKE EVERY OTHER BABY I'VE EVER SEEN
HE LOOKS EXACTLY LIKE EVERY OTHER BABY I'VE EVER SEEN
HE LOOKS EXACTLY LIKE EVERY OTHER BABY I'VE EVER SEEN
HE LOOKS EXACTLY LIKE EVERY OTHER BABY I'VE EVER SEEN

HE'S BEAUTIFUL!
HE LOOKS SO MUCH LIKE YOU.
OOH, DO YOU THINK SO?

Roasted
I SMOKE A BIT, YEAH?
AND IT'S LIKE, WHAT, A CLASS C NOW.
YEAH.

BUT I CAN BE ARRESTED IN SOME PLACES AND JUST CAUTIONED IN OTHERS AND HOW DO I KNOW WHICH IS WHICH?
EVEN THE POLICE AREN'T SURE.

AND THEY'RE MAKING IT MORE LEGAL BUT THEY'RE SPENDING MONEY TELLING ME IT'LL MAKE ME A PARANOID SCHIZOPHRENIC SO IS IT LIKE OKAY NOW SORT OF THING, OR IS IT, OR IS IT LIKE THEY'RE STILL SAYING IT'S YOU KNOW, NOT OKAY?

IT'S DAVID BLUNKETT'S MASTERPLAN.
HE WANTS TO MAKE THE STONERS EVEN MORE CONFUSED THAN THEY ALREADY ARE.
GOD. IT'S WORKING.
Andy Riley

Roasted
BIDDLY-DIP! BIDDLY-DIP!
SNOOZE
BIDDLY-DIP! BIDDLY-DIP!!
SNOOZE
BIDDLY-DIP!! BIDDLY-DIP!!
YOU'LL GIVE UP BEFORE I DO

Roasted
WHAT'S ON "ITV ONE?"

DID YOU SEE THAT THING ON "ITV ONE"?

STICK IT ON "ITV ONE," WILL YOU?
****

LOOK, IT DOESN'T MATTER HOW OFTEN ANT & DEC SAY IT. I CAN'T SAY IT. IT'S ITV. ITV. ITV.
YOU STOPPED CALLING A SNICKERS A MARATHON IN THE END.
IT TOOK NINE YEARS AND A LOT OF SOUL SEARCHING. I'M NOT GOING THROUGH THAT AGAIN.
**

HEY. KARL.
FANCY A STARBURST?
Andy RiLey

NOW ON BBC3 - LITTLE BRITAIN

FOLLOWED BY LITTLE BRITAIN, WITH LITTLE BRITAIN AT TEN...

...WARMING US UP FOR A WHOLE HOUR OF LITTLE BRITAIN
Andy Riley

Roasted
MOMENTS OF TIME YOU NEVER RECALL LATER ON, #29:
A
THE 15 SECONDS OF PURE ANXIETY WHEN NO "NEXT CUSTOMER PLEASE" SIGN IS AVAILABLE AND JUST ONE SLIPPING PIZZA BOX COULD MINGLE YOUR SHOPPING WITH THE NEXT PERSON'S

B
THE PURE, UNALLOYED RELIEF AS YOU FINALLY MARK YOUR TERRITORY
Andy Riley

Roasted
IS MARCH A BIT LATE TO BE SAYING "THIS IS JUST THE CHRISTMAS FAT I HAVEN'T LOST YET?"
NO.

HOW MUCH EMPHASIS DID I SAY THAT WITH?
AndyRiley

Roasted
Moments Of Life You Never Recall Later On, No.88
The Briefly Interesting Spam
>right click
>delete
>right click
>delete
>right click
>delete
>right click
>delete
>right click
>delete
>right click
>delete
>right click
>delete
>right click
>delete
>delete
>right click
>delete
>right click
>delete
>right click
>delete
>right click
>delete
>right click
>delete
>right click
>delete
>delete
>right click
>delete
>right click
>delete
>right click
>delete
>right click
>delete
Andy Riley

Roasted
DOING ANYTHING GOOD AT THE WEEKEND THEN?
I THINK I'LL SEE THE PASSION OF THE CHRIST.

HE DIES AT THE END, YOU KNOW.
DON'T SPOIL IT!!
Andy Riley

Roasted
I WENT TO SEE DAWN OF THE DEAD, RIGHT, AND THE ZOMBIES RUN!!
YOU CAN'T HAVE A RUNNING ZOMBIE!
KARL. KARL. KARL....

ZOMBIES AREN'T REAL.
YEAH. SURE OKAY, OKAY, BUT IF THEY WERE REAL, THEY'D SHUFFLE, WOULDN'T THEY? OBVIOUSLY!

HE'S RIGHT. NIGHT OF THE LIVING DEAD, THE ORIGINAL GEORGE A. ROMERO D.O.T.D..... ALWAYS A SHUFFLE. ALWAYS.
WHAT ABOUT 28 DAYS LATER? THAT'S GOT ZOMBIES WHO--

THEY'RE NOT ZOMBIES!! THEY'RE THE INFECTED!!

NEV, I'M STARTING TO FIGURE OUT WHY WE DON'T HAVE GIRLFRIENDS.
OH? WHY'S THAT?

DOING NOTHING ON SUNDAY AFTERNOON? THEN WHY NOT PLAY......

THE DIGITAL T.V. NAZI RELAY GAME!

Roasted
english science lesson

WHAT THE ENGLISH SAY IF THE WEATHER'S NICE:
AH.
A LOVELY ENGLISH SUMMER'S DAY.

WHAT THE ENGLISH SAY IF THE WEATHER'S NASTY:
HUH.
BRITISH WEATHER.

CONCLUSION: bad weather is somehow the fault of the welsh and the Scots
Andy Riley

Roasted
THERE. IF I KEEP A PICTURE OF ME LOOKING FAT ON THE FRONT OF THE FRIDGE, ONE I DON'T LIKE TO LOOK AT, IT'LL STOP ME EATING.

ON THE OTHER HAND:
WHEN I OPEN THE FRIDGE I DON'T HAVE TO LOOK AT THE PICTURE

Roasted
ARE YOU FROM
POLAND/LATVIA
ESTONIA/LITHUANIA
CYPRUS/MALTA/SLOV.
-AKIA/SLOVENIA/HUNG.
CZECH REP.?
WELCOME TO THE E.U.
PLEASE HELP
YOURSELF TO
MY JOB

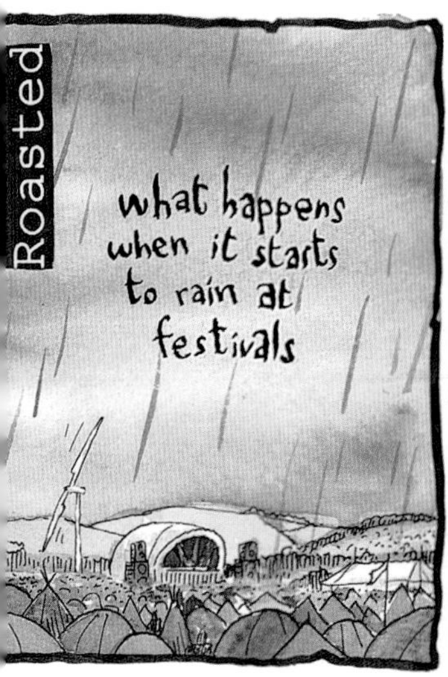
Roasted
what happens when it starts to rain at festivals

1. SINGER PROPOSES UNTENABLE POINT OF VIEW
DO WE CARE THAT IT'S RAINING??

2. CROWD GOES ALONG WITH IT
No!!
No!!
No!
NO!!
No!
No!
No!
No!!

3. TRUTH SINKS IN OVER NEXT FIVE SONGS
Andy Riley

Roasted
ON A DAY LIKE THIS, YOU THINK: SHOULD I REALLY BE SITTING INSIDE WATCHING BIG BROTHER?
OR SHOULD I SIT IN AND WATCH EURO 2004?

Roasted
THINGS TO DO ON A BLUSTERY DAY AT THE SEASIDE

GO TO AN ARCADE AND PLAY THEIR MOST UP-TO-DATE MACHINE
- BOUGHT IN 1996
Virtua COP

EAT ONE SHORTBREAD BISCUIT FROM THE TARTAN PLASTIC PACK OF TWO, THEN PUT THE OTHER ONE IN YOUR COAT POCKET TO EAT ON THE JOURNEY HOME
AND HAVE A LINING OF CRUMBS IN THE POCKET FOR THE NEXT 6 MONTHS

STAND ON THE FRONT FOR A BRACING GAME OF "GUESS WHERE THE SEA ENDS AND THE SKY BEGINS"
IT WAS REALLY NICE ON THURSDAY
YEAH I KNOW
Andy Riley

Roasted
LOTTIE, YOU REMEMBER MELANIE, DON'T YOU?
SURE. HI.
AAAAARG!

I HATE IT WHEN THIS HAPPENS.
IS SHE 4 MONTHS PREGNANT OR SLIGHTLY FATTER?
4 MONTHS PREGNANT OR SLIGHTLY FATTER?

CLUES. I NEED CLUES.
MINERAL WATER!

CONGRATULATIONS.
WHAT'S THE DUE DATE?

DAMN.
DAMN DAMN DAMN.

Roasted
FRIDAY NIGHT. FOUR BLOKES. TROUBLE.
DON'T CATCH ANYONE'S EYE... KEEP GOING.....

THEY DIDN'T NOTICE ME. THEY DIDN'T SEE ME.

OF COURSE!! I'VE GOT TOO OLD FOR THEM TO SEE!!
I'VE BECOME INVISIBLE TO 20 YEAR OLD MEN! I CAN WALK SAFELY AGAIN!!
WAHEY!!

Roasted
·YEAH.
YEAH, I TOOK THE WEEK OFF SICK.
THEN I WENT AND FELL ILL.

Roasted
THE HIGHWAY CODE FOR CYCLISTS

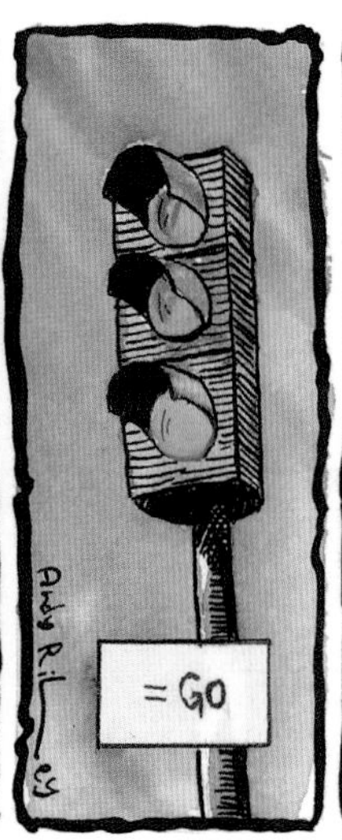
= GO

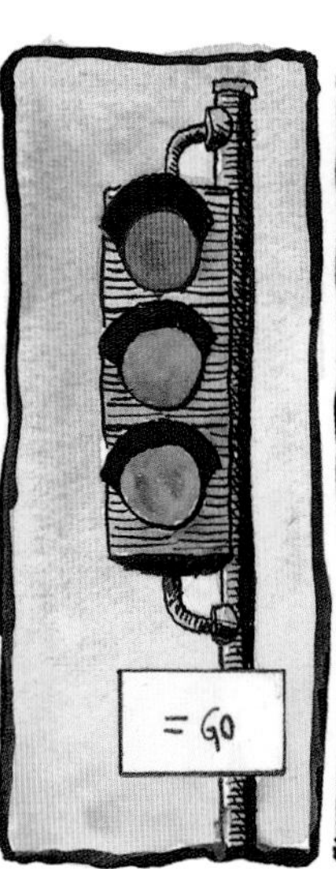
= GO

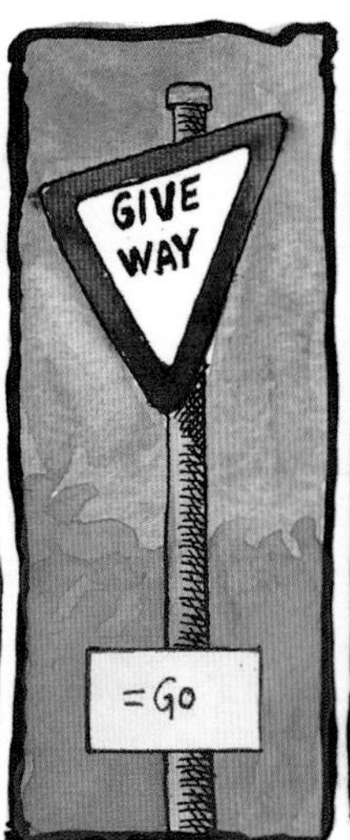
GIVE WAY
= GO

THIS IS A PAVEMENT. YOU KNOW, FOR WALKING ON.
= GO

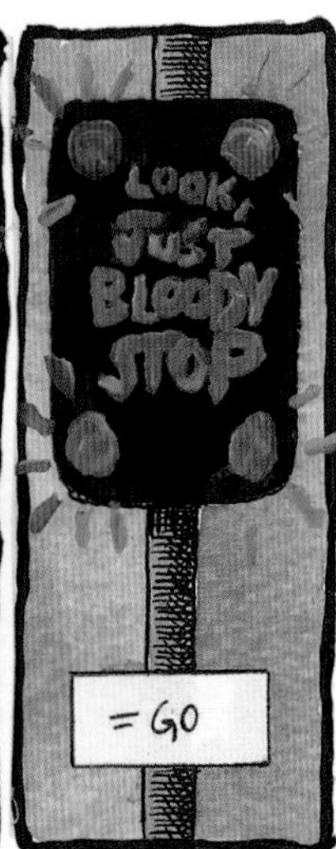
LOOK! JUST BLOODY STOP
= GO

x@#
= THE RESULT OF DECADES OF UNDER-INVESTMENT IN CYCLEPATHS

Roasted
I THINK MAYBE...
...THEY'RE STARTING TO RUN OUT OF STATES WHICH AIN'T KENTUCKY
NEW HAMPSHIRE FRIED CHICKEN
DISTRICT OF COLUMBIA FRIED CHICKEN
ALASKA FRIED CHICKEN
3 PCS £2.50
2 PC £2
HOT WINGS
SPICY WINGS
Andy Riley

LOOK NEV, IT'S JUST THAT IT'S WEIRD TALKING TO YOU WHEN YOU'RE WEARING THAT BLUETOOTH THING.
Andy Riley

IT LOOKS LIKE SOME MIND CONTROL DEVICE FROM A NIGHTMARE FUTURE SOCIETY.

IT MAKES YOU LOOK LIKE AN AGENT IN THE MATRIX.
A CYBORG.

I'LL BUY ONE FOR THE OTHER EAR

Roasted
Andy Riley
IT SAYS HERE WE'RE ALL BORROWING TOO MUCH.
IT SAYS THERE'S A DEBT TIME BOMB.
OH, WE CAN JUST STICK IT ON THE PILE. WITH THE PENSIONS TIME BOMB.

AND THE OBESITY TIME BOMB
AND THE INFERTILITY TIME BOMB.
AND THE AGING POPULATION TIME BOMB.
AND THE STD TIME BOMB.
AND THE ATLANTIC CONVEYOR TIME BOMB.
AND THE ENERGY TIME BOMB.

THAT'S A LOT OF TIME BOMBS.
JOURNALISTS OVER-USE IT. AND SOONER OR LATER ..... THEY'LL FIGURE THAT OUT.
IT'S A TIME BOMB.

Roasted
What they think we'll think
I DON'T MIND THAT SHE CUT IN FRONT OF ME.
SHE'S GOT A BABY ON BOARD SIGN IN HER CAR. SO I'M SURE SHE'S GOT A GOOD REASON.
BABY ON BOARD
SCREEECH!!

What we think
BABY ON BOARD
SCREEECH!!

Roasted
—BUT WHAT DO YOU THINK? PHONE US ON 0880 300 7733!! E-MAIL US!! OR TEXT US ON 83083!!

GO TO THE WEBSITE FOR A FULL TRACK LISTING, AND IF YOU CLICK ON "CHAT" YOU CAN TALK TO OTHER LISTENERS!
TELL US YOUR TRAVEL NEWS! OR YOU CAN--

(CLICK)

REMEMBER WHEN ALL THAT THE RADIO ASKED YOU TO DO WAS LISTEN?
Andy Riley 09

Roasted
idle thoughts
TO ENJOY WHENEVER YOU SHOULD BE WORKING

WHATEVER HAPPENED TO MAGIC EYE PICTURES?

WHAT DID THE FIRST EVER BAR CODE LOOK LIKE?
MAYBE SORT OF....
1

IF I PUT BOVRIL IN A SODA STREAM I COULD MAKE FIZZY BOVRIL WOULD THAT BE NICE OR JUST A BIT HORRIBLE
OR FIZZY MILK THAT WOULD BE STUPID
BUT NO MORE STUPID THAN FIZZY WATER

IF I PUT "GOOGLE" INTO GOOGLE....
MAYBE IT'LL EXPLODE !!
Andy Riley

Roasted
QUITE HOT TODAY.
YEP.
GLOBAL WARMING.

BUT THEY SAY IT'LL BE UNSEASONABLY COLD NEXT WEEK.
DUE TO UNPREDICTABLE WEATHER PATTERNS CAUSED BY GLOBAL WARMING.

SO...
...IF IT'S HOT THAT'S PROOF OF GLOBAL WARMING AND IF IT'S COLD, THAT'S PROOF OF GLOBAL WARMING TOO.
YEP! MODERN CLIMATOLOGY'S AN EASY SCIENCE!

Roasted
Fun for free,
No. 19
PIZZA-2-GO
Take back every pizza leaflet
that you've had through your
door in the last two years
Andy Riley

Roasted

Annoyance is:

Reading articles about
the wonders
of downshifting when you
haven't even managed
to upshift yet

Andy Riley

Roasted

REFLEXOLOGY.
IT'S AMAZING.
OH, IS IT.

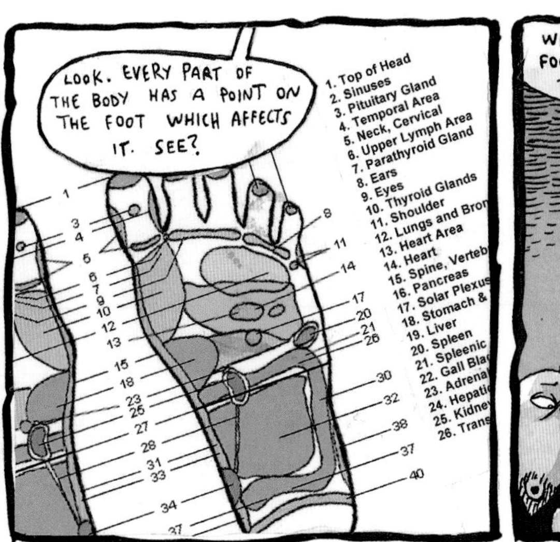
LOOK. EVERY PART OF THE BODY HAS A POINT ON THE FOOT WHICH AFFECTS IT. SEE?
1. Top of Head
2. Sinuses
3. Pituitary Gland
4. Temporal Area
5. Neck, Cervical
6. Upper Lymph Area
7. Parathyroid Gland
8. Ears
9. Eyes
10. Thyroid Glands
11. Shoulder
12. Lungs and Bron
13. Heart Area
14. Heart
15. Spine, Verteb
16. Pancreas
17. Solar Plexus
18. Stomach &
19. Liver
20. Spleen
21. Spleenic
22. Gall Bla
23. Adrenal
24. Hepati
25. Kidne
26. Trans

WHICH PART OF THE FOOT CORRESPONDS TO THE FOOT?
LET'S SEE...

OH.
THERE ISN'T ONE MARKED.
SO, IN REFLEXOLOGY, NO PART OF THE FOOT AFFECTS THE FOOT. HOW DOES THAT WORK THEN?
UM...

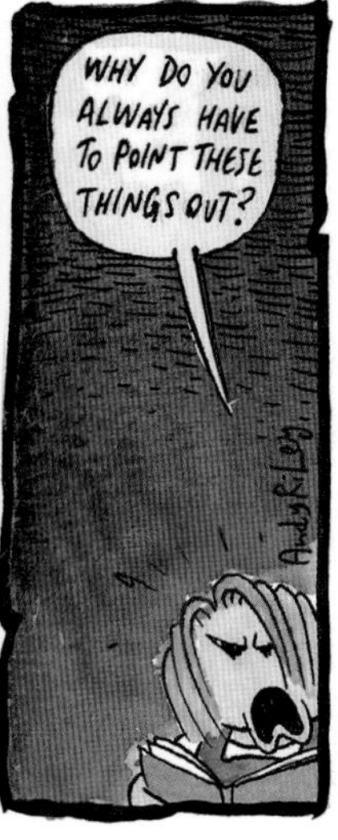
WHY DO YOU ALWAYS HAVE TO POINT THESE THINGS OUT?
AndyRiley

Roasted
MUM? HI.
LOOK, I'VE BEEN GIVING IT SOME THOUGHT AND I REALLY THINK THIS WHOLE BEING AN ADULT THING HASN'T WORKED OUT FOR ME.

I'LL BE OVER TOMORROW. I'LL WANT RAVIOLI AND CHIPS FOR TEA AND TOM AND JERRY ON THE TELLY AND A PLACE IN A LOCAL SCHOOL AND MY P.E. KIT PACKED.
DON'T ARGUE, PLEASE, MUM. I'VE MADE MY DECISION. I THINK YOU SHOULD RESPECT IT.

KLIK

THE NIGHTMARE IS OVER.

* OR ONE IN TWELVE, OR FIVE, OR TWENTY (ALL ARE ACCEPTABLE)

* OR FIVE PERCENT, OR FIFTEEN PERCENT, OR TWENTY PERCENT

* OR TWENTY FIVE, OR THIRTY, OR FIFTY OR SIXTY

* ADVANCED (4TH PINT) LEVEL ONLY

Roasted
WASH BASKET GEOLOGY
LAYER 1: WORN ALL THE TIME
LAYER 2: WORN ONCE A MONTH
LAYER 3: LAST WORN OR SEEN LAST YEAR
LAYER 4: GEOLOGICALLY STABLE SINCE 1999, WHEN THE WASH BASKET WAS BOUGHT
LAYER 5: ACTUALLY TRANSFERRED IN A DIRTY STATE FROM PREVIOUS WASH BASKET
LAYER 6: MID-NEOLITHIC. EVIDENCE OF MID-90s LIME GREEN TOPS
LAYER 7: EARLY CRETACEOUS
LAYER 8: PRE-CAMBRIAN UNDERPANTS

Roasted
"EVERY YEAR WE LOSE AN AREA OF RAIN FOREST THE SIZE OF WALES."

"AN ICEBERG THE SIZE OF WALES HAS BROKEN AWAY FROM THE ANTARCTIC ICE SHEET."

IT'S ALWAYS **WALES** WITH THESE THINGS, ISN'T IT?
YEP.
IT'S VERY THOUGHTFUL OF THE ENVIRONMENT TO COLLAPSE IN SUCH AN EASILY VISUALISABLE WAY.
Andy Riley

Roasted
AHHH. READY MEAL...
GLASS OF WINE.....
...DOCUMENTARY ABOUT A BRITISH FAMILY PLUNGING INTO DEBT AND DEPRESSION WHILE THEY DO UP A RUINED FARMHOUSE IN FRANCE.....
...HEAVEN.

Roasted
THIS WEEK, FORGET A USELESS FACT.
You probably know that the best way to escape a pursuing crocodile is to run in zig zags.
YOU WILL NEVER NEED TO KNOW THIS.
REMOVE IT FROM YOUR MIND.
This will make room for a fact you might use such as
"I really should get a pension."
Andy Riley

Roasted

"....IN THIS WAY, HIS WORK CHALLENGES OUR PRECONCEPTIONS."

BUT MY ONLY PRECONCEPTION WAS THAT I'D GET MY PRECONCEPTIONS CHALLENGED IN HERE.
Andy Riley

Roasted

"LOOK AT THOSE METROSEXUALS OVER THERE."

"OH, I KNOW THAT PUB. BIT OF A METROSEXUAL CROWD."

"WELL, THE WHOLE AREA'S CHANGED NOW. THE METROSEXUALS MOVED IN."

LOOK, IT DON'T MATTER WHAT JOURNALISTS SAY. YOU STILL CAN'T USE THE WORD IN AN ACTUAL SPOKEN SENTENCE.
THE IMPORTANT THING IS TO KEEP TRYING.
Andy Riley

Roasted
WHO'S YOUR HERO, KARL?
NURSES, SINGLE MOTHERS, FULL-TIME CARERS: THEY'RE **MY** HEROES.

YEAH, BUT REALLY.
OKAY, HANNIBAL FROM THE A-TEAM.

Roasted
WHAT DID YOU GET FOR CHRISTMAS, KARL?
OH, THE USUAL.
A HECTARE OF BIODIVERSE WETLAND PROTECTED IN MY NAME.

AH. THE SOAP ON A ROPE OF THE 21ST CENTURY.
THEY KEPT THE RECEIPT.
I CHANGED IT FOR SOCKS.

Roasted
HMM. HE'S JUST TALKING TO MY BREASTS.

THIS IS A GOOD BRA.

Roasted
WHAT'S ON?
WILDLIFE DOCUMENTARY.
AFRICA.

COME ON, WILDEBEEST!

RUN, WILDEBEEST! RUN FROM THE LION!
HANG ON...

IT'S CALLED "LION DIARY." WE'RE SUPPORTING THE LIONS TONIGHT.
THAT'S BETTER.
COME ON LION! YOUR CUBS ARE HUNGRY!
Andy Riley

Roasted
WELL, OF COURSE I'M STILL SMOKING.
THERE'S NO POINT EXTENDING MY LIFE BEFORE I'VE FIGURED OUT A WAY TO ENJOY IT.
Andy Riley

Roasted
HMM. HAVE I BEEN BURGLED?
OR HAVE I JUST NOT CLEANED UP FOR A WHILE?
Andy Riley

Roasted
I WON'T PICK UP. IT'LL JUST BE A FAKE PRIZE LINE.
ring ring
Andy Riley

ring ring

click
hi there, i'm calling from prizes direct.

AND TO THINK I USED TO NOT PICK UP CAUSE IT WAS BOUND TO BE MUM OR ONE OF MY FRIENDS.
WHAT AN INHUMAN WORLD IT'S BECOME.
some one in your house hold...

HI.... TAMSIN? COUGH

LOTTIE? ARE YOU ALL RIGHT?
YEAH. YEAH, I'M FINE. cough

I'M PHONING IN SICK IN A MINUTE SO I JUST cough HAD TO PRACTICE MY **WEAK VOICE.** cough

IT'S VERY GOOD. THROW IN A FEW COUGHS AT THE **START** OF THE SENTENCE THOUGH.
cough THANKS.
cough SEE YOU AT ONE.
METHOD ACTOR.
IT'S THE ONLY WAY TO GET IT RIGHT. cough

ROASTED
WHAT'S WRONG?
IT SAYS HERE YOUR FIVE PORTIONS OF FRUIT AND VEG DOESN'T INCLUDE POTATOES.

EH?
SO FIVE-A-DAY DOESN'T INCLUDE MASH?
NO!
OR CHIPS. SURELY CHIPS.
NO!!

BUT POTATOES ARE VEGETABLES!
I KNOW!

BUT THEY'RE THE NICE VEGETABLES.
THAT'S WHY THEY DON'T COUNT.
NOT FAIR.
Andy Riley

Roasted
UNHEALTHY TROLLEYLOAD
PIE
PIE
GARLIC BREAD
PIZZA
LASAGNE
WINE
CRISPS
CHOCOLATE
CRISPS
CURRY
NEXT CUSTOMER

+ ONE PROMINENTLY PLACED GREEN VEGETABLE

= ACCEPTABLY HEALTHY-LOOKING TROLLEYLOAD
Andy Riley
PIE
PIE
GARLIC BREAD
PIZZA
LASAGNE
WINE
CRISPS
SWISS ROLL
BUTTER
CHOCOLATE
CRISPS
CURRY
NEXT CUSTOMER

Roasted
I DOWNLOADED AN EPISODE OF THE SOPRANOS OFF THE NET YESTERDAY.

IS THAT ILLEGAL?
YEAH.
BUT I'M AFRAID EXPOSURE TO TV SHOWS GLAMOURISING GANGSTERS HAS ERODED MY MORAL VALUES TO A POINT WHERE I NO LONGER CARE.

Roasted
WAR!!
HUH!!
WHAT IS IT GOOD FOR?

RIDDING EUROPE OF FASCISM IN THE 1940s.

WELL...
THERE IS THAT I SUPPOSE.
AndyRiLey

Roasted
LANCE ARMSTRONG ANTI-CANCER WRISTBAND
ANTI-BULLYING WRISTBAND
ANTI-HOOLIGANISM WRISTBAND
STOP POVERTY WRISTBAND
ENVIRONMENTALISM WRISTBAND
WRISTBAND SUPPORTING UNEMPLOYED PEOPLE WHO USED TO MAKE RIBBONS FOR THIS KIND OF THING
Andy Riley

Roasted

I HAD A MAD TIME IN STOCKHOLM BUT I WON'T GO ON ABOUT THAT CAUSE YOU READ IT ALL ON MY BLOG, YEAH?

AND THEN, GOD!!
ALL THAT STUFF WITH MY MUM!!
BUT YOU'VE READ MY BLOG SO YOU KNOW ALL THAT.

AND THE STUFF ABOUT MOVING HOUSE....
I BLOGGED A LOT ABOUT THAT, DIDN'T I?
I'LL JUST NOD.
Andy Riley

Roasted
1 APPLY HOT WAX TO CHEST

2 PLACE FABRIC STRIPS ON WAX

3 GRIP END OF STRIP BETWEEN THUMB AND FOREFINGER

4 BOTTLE IT

5 GO TO PUT A SHIRT ON
WHO'S EVER GOING TO SEE YOU BARE-CHESTED ANYWAY
WELL... AT LEAST I DON'T HAVE A HAIRY BACK
Andy Riley

Wednesday
DAMN!
IT'S A LINK MACHINE.

IT'S ALL LINK MACHINES NOW AND THEY BURN YOU FOR A QUID FIFTY.
HAHA!! I'LL TAKE OUT TWICE AS MUCH AS I NEED SO THAT'LL SAVE ME 75p.

JUST SO LONG AS I DON'T SPEND IT TWICE AS FAST CAUSE IT'S SITTING THERE IN MY POCKET.

Thursday
LINK

Roasted
BIDDLY DIP
BIDDLY DIP

GOD.

JIMMY CARR EVEN DOES LINKS FOR MY DREAMS NOW.

Roasted
VATERST

I DON'T CARE HOW MANY THEY PUT IN FRONT OF ME.
I'LL STILL NEVER READ IT.
THEY WON'T BREAK ME.
THE DA VINCI CODE
Andy Riley

Roasted
GOD.
SHOULD I BE DOING THIS? BOOKING ON A BUDGET AIRLINE?
TK TK TK

THEY'RE THE BIGGEST GROWTH AREA FOR GREENHOUSE GAS EMISSIONS AND WE ALL CONSPIRE TO IGNORE IT.
WE'RE WRECKING THE WORLD FOR OUR CHILDREN – FOR THE SAKE OF A MINI-BREAK.

HAHA!! BUT THE FLIGHT IS TICKETLESS SO THAT SAVES ON PAPER SO THAT'S GOOD FOR THE ENVIRONMENT!!
AND COME ON... A TENNER TO MADRID...
TK TK TK TK TK TK TK TK TK TK TK TK

Roasted

WHILE AWAY TUESDAY NIGHTS WITH THE.......

t.v. childcare show cliché checklist

TICK THE BOXES TO SCORE THE POINTS!

CHILDCARE EXPERT WATCHES FOOTAGE AND SAYS "THIS IS GOING TO BE TOUGH" .... ☐ 2 POINTS

SHOT OF CHILDCARE EXPERT WALKING PURPOSEFULLY .... ☐ 1 POINT

"GET A BED-TIME ROUTINE WITH A STORY"..... ☐ 2 POINTS

"HAVE SET MEALTIMES".......... ☐ 2 POINTS

ELDER DAUGHTER HITS YOUNGER DAUGHTER WITH PLASTIC BRICK.......... ☐ 3 POINTS

MOTHER CRIES TO CAMCORDER AT 3.30 AM... ☐ 1 POINT

"IGNORE THOSE TANTRUMS... ☐ 1 POINT

...AND REWARD GOOD BEHAVIOUR" ☐ 1 POINT

"MUM AND DAD NEED THEIR TIME TOO".... ☐ 2 POINTS

CHILDREN, NOW IMMACULATELY BEHAVED, PRESENT A PARTING GIFT TO CHILDCARE EXPERT.... ☐ 3 POINTS

PARENTS THANK EXPERT: EXPERT SAYS "NO, YOU SHOULD THANK YOURSELVES"..... ☐ 1 POINT

30 MINUTES UP!! WRITE YOUR TOTAL SCORE HERE ________ THEN TURN OVER + WATCH A PROPERTY SHOW

Roasted
WHAT DO YOU THINK?
BIT MUCH ON A FIRST DATE?
OVULATING NOW

Roasted
SO C3PO GETS A MEMORY WIPE AT THE END OF EPISODE III, BUT OBI-WAN DOESN'T, SO NOW COME IN EPISODE IV HE ACTS LIKE HE'S NEVER MET C3PO?
CAUSE HE DOESN'T WANT TO HURT C3PO'S FEELINGS. FINDING OUT YOU'VE HAD A MEMORY WIPE MUST BE VERY TRAUMATIC FOR A DROID AND HE KNOWS HOW HIGHLY STRUNG C3PO IS.

BUT R2D2 DOESN'T GET A MEMORY WIPE, AND HE NEVER LETS ON TO LUKE THAT HE FOUGHT IN THE BATTLES OF NABOO AND CORUSCANT WITH LUKE'S FATHER.
YES. UNLESS.... HE WAS SAYING IT ALL THE WAY THROUGH EPISODES IV, V AND VI BUT C3PO DELIBERATELY NEVER TRANSLATED IT TO AVOID UPSETTING LUKE.
NOW, WHEN YOU SEE THE DEATH STAR AT THE END...

NEV!! WOMAN APPROACHING. TOPIC CHANGE.
HIYA LOTTIE. WE WERE JUST TALKING ABOUT BREASTS AND FOOTBALL.
THAT'S RIGHT.
Andy Riley

Roasted
MOST PEOPLE ARE STILL SO UPTIGHT ABOUT SEX.
YEAH.

IT'S JUST, LIKE.... WHY AREN'T WE A BIT MORE OPEN ABOUT OUR SEXUALITY?
YEAH.

I HAVE BETTER ORGASMS IF I IMAGINE THE PERSON I'M WITH IS THE SQUIDGY BIT INSIDE A DALEK.
AND, YOU KNOW, IT'S OKAY TO SAY STUFF LIKE THAT.

Andy Riley

Roasted

THE NEGLECTED URBAN GARDEN

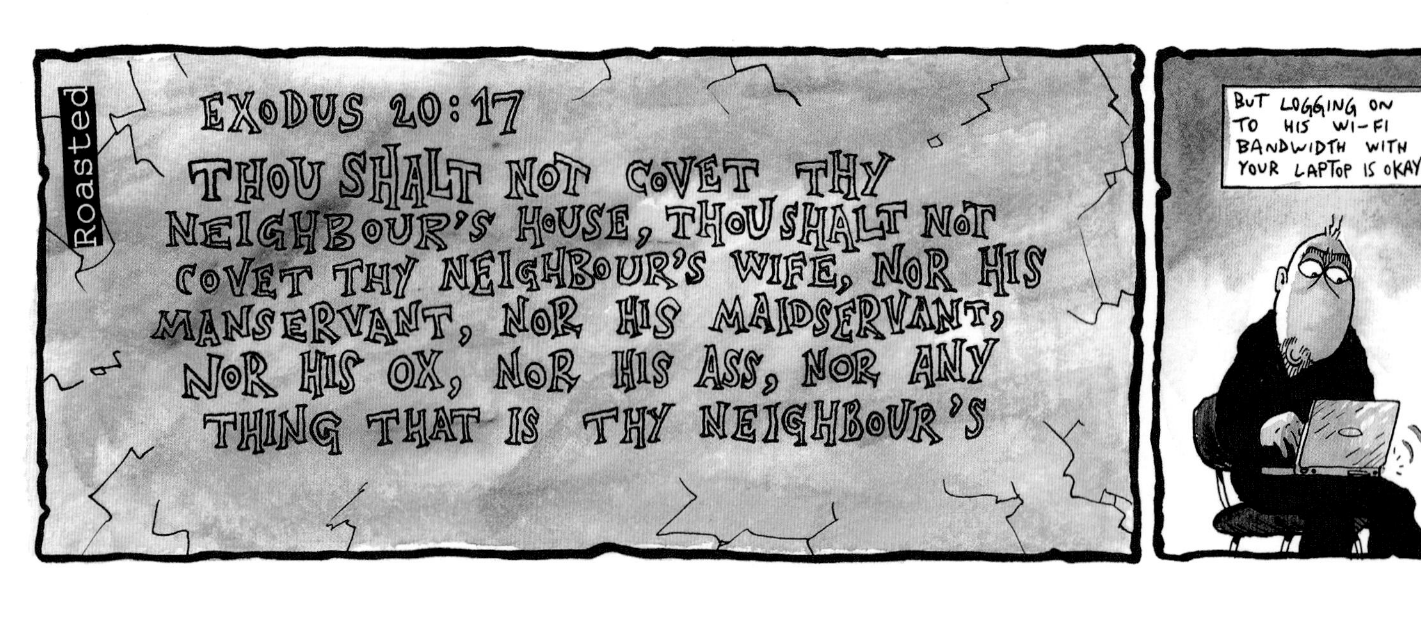
Roasted
EXODUS 20:17
THOU SHALT NOT COVET THY NEIGHBOUR'S HOUSE, THOU SHALT NOT COVET THY NEIGHBOUR'S WIFE, NOR HIS MANSERVANT, NOR HIS MAIDSERVANT, NOR HIS OX, NOR HIS ASS, NOR ANY THING THAT IS THY NEIGHBOUR'S
BUT LOGGING ON TO HIS WI-FI BANDWIDTH WITH YOUR LAPTOP IS OKAY

OH. ANOTHER STEAMY TV LESBIAN KISS.
YOU GET ONE EVERY FIVE MINUTES NOW.
HMPH.

WHERE WERE THEY ALL WHEN I WAS FOURTEEN?
Andy Riley

WHY AREN'T THERE LAUNDERETTES FOR DISHES?

Roasted
I THINK I MIGHT BE HAVING A QUARTER-LIFE CRISIS.
OH, DON'T WORRY.
YOU'RE TOO OLD FOR ONE OF THOSE NOW.

THAT DIDN'T HELP, DID IT?
NOT REALLY, NO.
Andy Riley

...SO THIS WAS ABOUT, OOOH, 2001, 2002...
I'LL TELL HER I'M BISEXUAL. IT'LL MAKE ME SOUND MORE INTERESTING.
Andy Riley
DROP IT IN CASUAL.... DROP IT IN CASUAL....
SO AT THE TIME I WAS SHARING A FLAT WITH THESE TWO OTHER BISEXUAL GUYS....
YOU'RE BISEXUAL?
I DON'T LIKE TO DEFINE MYSELF, BUT YEAH...
SHE THINKS I'M BISEXUAL! I'M IN!!
I'LL TELL HIM I'M BISEXUAL. IT'LL MAKE ME SOUND MORE INTERESTING.

CHANGING ROOMS
ONLY 3 ITEMS
THAT YOU CAN'T AFFORD,
YOU WON'T FIT INTO
AND YOU COULDN'T CARRY
OFF EVEN IF YOU DID
AT ONE TIME
Andy RiLey

EPISODE ONE THEY'RE ON AN ISLAND	EPISODE TWO YEP, THEY'RE STILL ON THE ISLAND	EPISODE THREE YEP, THEY'RE STILL ON THE ISLAND	EPISODE FOUR YEP, THEY'RE STILL ON THE ISLAND	EPISODE FIVE YEP, THEY'RE STILL ON THE ISLAND	EPISODE SIX YEP, THEY'RE STILL ON THE ISLAND	EPISODE SEVEN YEP, THEY'RE STILL ON THE ISLAND	EPISODE EIGHT YEP, THEY'RE STILL ON THE ISLAND
EPISODE NINE YEP, THEY'RE STILL ON THE ISLAND	EPISODE TEN YEP, THEY'RE STILL ON THE ISLAND	EPISODE ELEVEN YEP, THEY'RE STILL ON THE ISLAND	EPISODE TWELVE YEP, THEY'RE STILL ON THE ISLAND	EPISODE THIRTEEN YEP, THEY'RE STILL ON THE ISLAND	EPISODE FOURTEEN YEP, THEY'RE STILL ON THE ISLAND	EPISODE FIFTEEN YEP, THEY'RE STILL ON THE ISLAND	EPISODE SIXTEEN YEP, THEY'RE STILL ON THE ISLAND
EPISODE SEVENTEEN YEP, THEY'RE STILL ON THE ISLAND	EPISODE EIGHTEEN YEP, THEY'RE STILL ON THE ISLAND	EPISODE NINETEEN YEP, THEY'RE STILL ON THE ISLAND	EPISODE TWENTY YEP, THEY'RE STILL ON THE ISLAND	EPISODE TWENTY ONE YEP, THEY'RE STILL ON THE ISLAND	EPISODE TWENTY TWO YEP, THEY'RE STILL ON THE ISLAND	EPISODE TWENTY THREE YEP, THEY'RE STILL ON THE ISLAND	EPISODE TWENTY FOUR YEP, THEY'RE STILL ON THE ISLAND

Roasted
Andy Riley

"BLACK IS IN....
...AGAIN?"

LOTTIE!! WHEN WERE BLACK CLOTHES OUT?
OOH, ABOUT 2000 TILL JUST RECENTLY.
AND JUST WHEN WERE YOU PLANNING TO TELL ME?
BAM

R·o·a·s·t·e·d
THUNK
CHICKEN TIKKA MASALA

SKRRRAKKK
CHICKEN TIKKA MASALA

SO WHY ARE THEY CALLED READY MEALS?
CHICKEN TIKKA MASALA

Roasted
WHAT YOU GOT PLANNED FOR THE WEEKEND THEN?
A LIE-IN.
AH. BINGE RESTING.

THEN GO FOR A HIKE.
BINGE WALKING.

WHY DOES EVERYTHING GET "BINGE" ON THE FRONT NOW?
DUNNO.

I MEAN, WHERE DID IT COME FROM?
THAT'S TWO QUESTIONS.
THAT'S BINGE ASKING.
Andy Riley

Roasted
I DID EVERYTHING I SET OUT TO DO TODAY.
WHAT WAS THAT THEN?

FORGET ALL THE THINGS I WAS MEANT TO DO YESTERDAY.
WHICH WERE?
NO IDEA!
GOD, I'M GOOD.

Roasted

WAZZZUUUUU UUUUUUUP?

WEST SIDE.

NEV, I KNOW WE LIVE IN A HYPER-ACCELERATED CULTURE DEVOURING ITS OWN HISTORY AT AN UNPRECEDENTED RATE...
...BUT IT'S STILL TOO SOON FOR AN EARLY NOUGHTIES REVIVAL.
HMPH. IS IT COS I IS BLACK?
AndyRiley

Roasted
I'VE GOT TO CHOOSE WHETHER I GO TO MY MUM'S OR MY DAD'S FOR CHRISTMAS.

THAT'S ALWAYS A TOUGH ONE.
I KNOW.
WHO DO I WANT TO DISAPPOINT THE MOST?

Roasted
I'M NOT GOING TO GET OFF WITH YOU AT THE WORK CHRISTMAS PISS-UP AGAIN, YOU KNOW.
MM-HMM.

IT ONLY HAPPENED CAUSE I WAS DRUNK.
IT'S NOT HAPPENING AGAIN.
RIGHT.
JUST SO YOU KNOW.
SURE.

SO DON'T TRY IT AGAIN.
WON'T. IT WAS A BIG MISTAKE.
NOT HAPPENING AGAIN.
RIGHT.
GOOD.

WHAT DO YOU MEAN, "BIG MISTAKE?"
Andy RiLEY

Roasted
The precise moment when Karl realises he may never again have a girlfriend with larger breasts than his own
Andy Riley

Roasted
SHIT.
WHERE'S MY...
....SHIT.
SHIT.
PAT
PAT
PAT
PAT
PAT
PAT
SHIT.
SHIT SHIT
SHIT. SHIT SHIT
SHIT SHIT SHIT
SHIT SHIT.
AAAHHH!!
AHA. HAHA.
AHAHAHAHAHA HA.
HA HA HA HA.
WHY CAN'T
ORGASMS FEEL AS
GOOD AS FINDING
YOUR WALLET?
Andy Riley

Roasted
BACK TO YOU LUCY. AND DON'T FORGET.....
IT'S ONLY.... ...GIGGLE.....
296 SHOPPING DAYS TILL NEXT CHRISTMAS!
IT JUST AIN'T CHRISTMAS TILL THEY DO THAT JOKE ON THE REGIONAL NEWS
HAHAHAHA ...THANKS PAUL.
...NINE TIMES

HA!! DID YOU KNOW A McDONALD'S SALAD'S GOT MORE CALORIES THAN A BIG MAC?
WELL IT HAS!

YEAH, BUT THAT INCLUDES THE DRESSING AND THE CRUTONS AND HE'S ONLY PUT ON A LITTLE BIT OF BOTH.

PLUS MOST PEOPLE HAVE FRIES WITH A BIG MAC BUT NOT WITH THE SALAD. HE'S THE SAME. SO, YOU KNOW, IT'S NOT A COMPLETELY FAIR POINT.

KARL. I KNOW YOUR POLITICS ARE BROADLY LIBERAL SO WHEN I SLAG OFF McDONALD'S I EXPECT YOU TO JOIN IN.
SORRY, SORRY...

Roasted
8.15 A.M.

A DOUBLE SEAT!!

PUT BAG NEXT TO ME.....
THEN PRETEND TO BE ASLEEP....

PERSONAL SPACE JACKPOT!!

SCUSE ME? IS THAT SEAT FREE?
YAWN ...SORRY, I'LL MOVE THESE...
DAMN!!

Roasted
IT'S NOT A BEER BELLY.
IT'S A ONE PACK.
Andy Riley

Roasted
THAI CURRY....
PRICK
PRICK
PRICK

PASTA
BAKE....
PRICK
PRICK
PRICK
PRICK

.....READY MEAL
FUSION CUISINE.
GOD, I'M
SOPHISTICATED.
Andy Riley

Roasted
FRIDAY SHOULD COME SOONER.

MAYBE THERE'S A WAY TO PUT THE DAYS OF THE WEEK ON "SHUFFLE"....

"I CAN'T BELIEVE YOU'VE NEVER SEEN...."

— A GAME FOR A MAN AND A WOMAN
— PICK FROM THE LIST BELOW OR ADD YOUR OWN!

THE DIRTY DOZEN
ALIENS
THE LIMEY
THE FEATURE LENGTH SWEENEY
DEMOLITION MAN
MAD MAX
MAD MAX II
SEXY BEAST
IN WHICH WE SERVE
DAWN OF THE DEAD
RUMBLEFISH
TEAM AMERICA
DESPERADO
PITCH BLACK
CUBE
DAS BOOT
STARSHIP TROOPERS
THE GENERAL

GANGS OF NEW YORK
THE SOUTH PARK FILM
PI
THE ORIGINAL LUC BESSON "TAXI"
VANISHING POINT
ZARDOZ
GOODFELLAS
EL MARIACHI
CLERKS
HARD BOILED
AKIRA
WAY OF THE DRAGON
ESCAPE TO VICTORY
THIS IS SPINAL TAP
ROLLERBALL
FASTER, PUSSYCAT, KILL! KILL!

MAN BITES DOG
THE FOOTBALL FACTORY
GANGSTER NO. 1
SILENT RUNNING
PASSENGER 57
SATURN 3
BAD TASTE
DOG SOLDIERS
REIGN OF FIRE
HEAD
28 DAYS LATER
CAPRICORN ONE
THE RIGHT STUFF
PLAN 9 FROM OUTER SPACE
CASINO
ROCKY III
DELIVERANCE

Roasted
...THOUGH, YOU KNOW, I THINK JAKE GILLHALLING'S THE BEST THING IN IT.

JAKE JILLINGHAM?

JAKE GEHELLALL.
JAKE GLYNNEN-HILL?

JAKE GALLIONELLE.
GARALLAAL-ILLEN.
JAKE GAALNALL.
JAKE GILLAN.
GLANDA-LAAH.
JAKE GLENDA-HALAL.

I'VE CHANGED MY MIND.
I LIKE HEATH LEDGER.

Roasted
ninth pint resolutions

I'M GOING TO BUY A COTTAGE IN THE HEBRIDES
OR FIJI I BEEN THERE IT'S NICE

I'LL TRAIN FOR THE LONDON MARATHON NO F██ IT EVERYONE DOES THAT I'LL TRAIN FOR THE SKELETON BOB FOUR YEARS TO GET GOOD THAT SOUNDS RIGHT THEN I RECKON GOLD CAUSE IT'S AN EASY MEDAL THAT BRITISH WOMAN HAD ONLY BEEN DOIN IT ABOUT A WEEK

I'M GOING TO WRITE A NOVEL AT WEEKENDS SHOULD TAKE FOUR MONTHS I RECKON AND IT'LL BE BASED ON MY LIFE MY LIFE'S BEEN PRETTY MENTAL WE'LL ALL BE CHARACTERS IN IT AND IT'S ABOUT A GROUP OF FRIENDS WHO HAVE TO KILL A MAN

I'LL DEFINITELY BE GOING HOME AFTER THE NEXT ONE
Andy Riley

Roasted
WILDEBEEST. MICROSCOPE. BRACKEN. CONSTELLATION. DONCASTER. TURBAN. ANTARCTICA. VELODROME.

ÜBERMENSCH. HOLDFAST. ANTHRACITE. SAAB - GRIPPEN. HEPTATHLON. INTEGER. TURKMENISTAN.

RESTITUTION. CALLISTO. ARTESIAN. HARPSICHORD. PHOTOSYNTHESIS. BEGUILE. HOMINID.

I'M SORRY SIR, NONE OF THOSE MATCH WITH THE BANKING PASSWORD I'VE GOT HERE....
DON'T YOU DARE HANG UP!

I'LL GET IT SOON. LAW OF AVERAGES.
BELLJAR. CONSTANTINOPLE. MOHOROVICIC. FRIGATE. SYCAMORE....

Roasted
IF WE ALL STOP THINKING AND TALKING ABOUT NOEL EDMONDS.....
MAYBE HE'LL DISAPPEAR AGAIN

EMPTY YOUR MIND....
EMPTY YOUR MIND....

AGH!
Andy Riley

Roasted
27 hours
41 minutes

= the average time lapse between getting in a row with a total stranger and thinking up the perfect riposte to the last thing he said
AndyRiley

Roasted
DATE
LOOK, PLEASE DON'T TAKE THIS THE WRONG WAY, BUT.....
AFTER LISTENING TO YOU FOR JUST TWENTY MINUTES I WANT TO SLAM YOUR HEAD IN A CAR DOOR THEN CUT OFF YOUR LEG AND BEAT YOU TO DEATH WITH IT THEN MAKE THOUSANDS OF CLONES OF YOU AND KILL ONE EVERY DAY BY A DIFFERENT METHOD
OH, I'VE UPSET YOU NOW HAVEN'T I? THAT'S A SHAME
WELL?
BETTER THAN THE LAST TWO

BAD POSTURE
TOO WRINKLY TO LOOK STUDENT
TOO FAT TO LOOK INDIE
LOOKS LESS COOL AS YOU GET OLDER
Andy Riley

Roasted

I COULD THROW AWAY THIS ALUMINIUM SCOOTER IF IT DIDN'T SUBCONSCIOUSLY REPRESEN MY OPTIMISTIC NINETIES SELF
AndyRil

NEXT WEEK: "EINSTEIN WAS DYSLEXIC, YOU KNOW"

Roasted
GOD. A LIST SHOW. FIFTY BEST WHATEVER. THEY'RE ALWAYS WRONG.
I HATE LIST SHOWS.
YEP.

AND I'M GOING TO SIT HERE AND CARRY ON HATING IT FOR THE NEXT THREE HOURS.
YEP.
Andy Riley

Roasted
KARL'S FOOTBALL KNOWLEDGE

PRE-WORLD CUP
****
DURING WORLD CUP
THEY'RE WEAK AT THE BACK
THEY'RE PLAYING WITH ONE UP FRONT WHICH IS VERY SURPRISING FOR THEM
HE HASN'T GOT THE SERVICE SO YOU CAN'T BLAME HIM
HE'S GOT TO UP THE TEMPO IN THE SECOND HALF, GET AN ATTACKING MIDFIELDER ON
TOO MANY LONG BALLS
THEY'RE DANGEROUS ON SET PIECES
YOU CAN'T SIT BACK ON A ONE GOAL LEAD
****
POST-WORLD CUP
****
Andy Riley

Roasted

BIG BROTHER "BEING MYSELF" BINGO

A GAME FOR TWO OR MORE PLAYERS ON BIG BROTHER EVICTION NIGHTS

- Each player picks a 'minute number' between one and thirty
- When the evicted housemate sits down for the Davina interview, start the clock
- Note the minute when the evicted housemate congratulates themselves on the vacuous, facile, narcissistic achievement of 'being myself'
- The player with the nearest number wins

Roasted
OH GOD OH GOD IT'S GOING TO SAY I'M PREGNANT I KNOW IT WILL IT'LL SAY I'M PREGNANT

I'M NOT PREGNANT!

OH GOD OH GOD I'M INFERTILE I MUST BE OH GOD I KNOW I'M INFERTILE
Andy Riley

Roasted
"BANGALORE BREAK"
— THE 6 SECONDS THAT PASS BETWEEN YOU PICKING UP THE PHONE AND THE PHONE CONNECTING TO THE CALL CENTRE IN INDIA
SEE ALSO: LUCKNOW LULL, GANGES FREEZE
Andy Riley

DO YOU FANCY HIM?

NO

GO HOME AND WATCH THE O.C.

YES

HE DOESN'T FANCY YOU THOUGH

Andy Riley

Roasted
PAPER WASTE
FOOD WASTE
GLASS WASTE
PLASTIC WASTE

PAPER WASTE
PLASTIC WASTE

SO IT WAS MY BIRTHDAY ON SATURDAY AND HE GOT ME CARNATIONS.
MM.
YEP.
FINISHED WITH HIM ON TUESDAY.

CARNATIONS. HIM ALL OVER REALLY.
YEAH.
MM.

WHICH ONES ARE CARNATIONS?
IF YOU HAVE TO ASK THAT ..
....THEN THEY'RE THE ONES YOU ALWAYS BUY.
YEEAHH.

Roasted
IT'S OUR DUTY TO DEFY THEM.
MAKING US AFRAID: THAT'S THE WHOLE POINT OF IT. THAT'S WHY IT'S CALLED TERRORISM.

SO WE SHOW THEM WE'RE NOT AFRAID. WE SHOW THEM WE'RE GOING TO CARRY ON.
IF WE KEEP TRAVELLING, WE KEEP WINNING.

NO, YOU CAN'T BUNK OFF ON HOLIDAY FOR THE WEEK JUST CAUSE RYANAIR ARE DOING DISCOUNTS.
YOU'RE PLAYING INTO THEIR EVIL HANDS!!

A CONSPIRACY THEORIST:

AN INTELLIGENT PERSON WHO BELIEVES NOTHING HE READS IN THE PAPERS

AND EVERYTHING HE READS ON THE INTERNET

Roasted
I WENT TO SEE "AN INCONVENIENT TRUTH."
ME TOO. WOW.
YEAH.

I'M GOING TO DO MY BIT BY FEELING SLIGHTLY MORE GUILTY ABOUT MY NEXT BUDGET FLIGHT.
I THOUGHT IT WAS SO GOOD I DROVE THE LONG WAY HOME TO EMIT MORE CARBON SO HE'LL DO A SEQUEL.

Play

GUESS THE LIBERAL DAILY's WALLCHART

- fun for lefties, six days a week!

- uses tons more paper, thus bad for the environment, adding extra liberal guilt (perfect for Independent readers)

ROASTED
BLOODY HELL
I'VE GOT EVERY PROBLEM IN THE WORLD
EXCEPT WORKAHOLISM AND ANOREXIA
YEP..... SAFE THERE

KARL TRIES TO SEND AN ANGRY DRUNK TEXT
BUT FORGETS HIS PREDICTIVE TEXT HASN'T GOT SWEARING

your so full of shiv

dual you

THERE

THAT'LL SHOW HIM

your a dublin aunt

Roasted
ETHICAL SHOPPING
THIS ONE'S DEFINITELY GOOD FOR THE ENVIRONMENT
IT'S GOT A LOGO WITH A TREE IN IT

Roasted
FACING A DIFFICULT ISSUE? FEEL LIKE YOU'D RATHER DODGE IT? THEN MAKE LIKE A LABOUR MINISTER AND......
CALL FOR A PUBLIC DEBATE

I CALL FOR A PUBLIC DEBATE ON ME TURNING UP TO WORK DRUNK

YES, I DO OWE YOU FIFTY POUNDS, AND IT'S TIME THERE WAS A PUBLIC DEBATE ABOUT THAT

SURELY A PUBLIC DEBATE ON THE FACT I'M SLEEPING WITH YOUR GIRLFRIEND IS NOW UNAVOIDABLE

CALL FOR A PUBLIC DEBATE TODAY!
IT WORKED FOR JACK STRAW, MAKE IT WORK FOR YOU!
andy riley

Roasted
I THINK FOR A LONG TIME NOW JOURNALISTIC CLICHES HAVE BEEN THE ELEPHANT IN THE ROOM.

BUT MAYBE..... ....MAYBE CLICHES HAVE REACHED A TIPPING POINT.

SO... ARE YOU SAYING...
YES.
I'M SAYING IT'S A WAKE UP CALL FOR CLICHES.

WELL, I WISH ANYWAY.
I'M WAITING TILL THE EXACT MOMENT THE TIPPING POINT CONCEPT FALLS OUT OF STYLE, THEN I'LL SAY, "OOH LOOK, THE TIPPING POINT'S REACHED A TIPPING POINT."
Andy Riley

Roasted
THERE'S NO SUCH THING AS FRIENDS
JUST STRANGERS I HAVEN'T FALLEN OUT OF TOUCH WITH YET

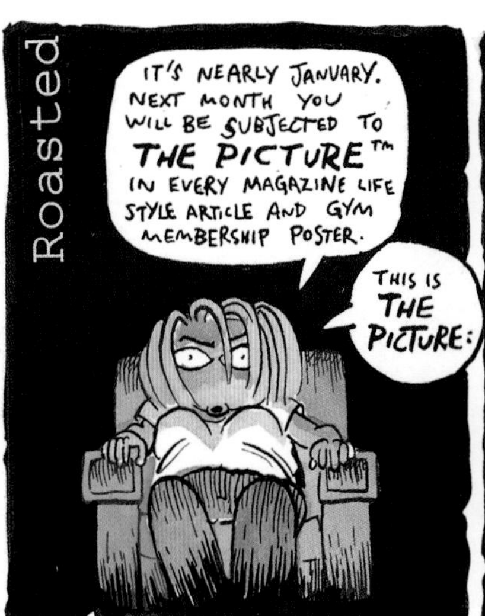
Roasted
IT'S NEARLY JANUARY. NEXT MONTH YOU WILL BE SUBJECTED TO THE PICTURE™ IN EVERY MAGAZINE LIFE STYLE ARTICLE AND GYM MEMBERSHIP POSTER.
THIS IS THE PICTURE:

skinny woman jumping in the air
CLENCHED FIST SHOWS TRIUMPH & PRIDE
BARE MIDRIFF FLAUNTS WEIGHT LOSS
HEELS HIGHER THAN KNEES: INDICATES FITNESS AND AGILITY
LONG TANNED LEGS: SEE ABOVE
SUMMERY SURROUNDINGS INDICATE THIS IS NOT HAPPENING IN JANUARY. IMPLICATION: THIS IMAGE COULD BE YOU IN 6 MONTHS.

DON'T LET THEM MANIPULATE YOU.
HAVE A CHOCOLATE MOUSSE.
FIGHT THE PICTURE.

Roasted
SHOPS ALL SOLD OUT OF NINTENDO WII?
DIDN'T TRACK ONE DOWN IN TIME FOR CHRISTMAS?
1 APPLY ELASTOPLAST TO ELBOWS
2 SMASH HEAD ON CORNER OF DOOR
THWOK
3 RESURFACE KNUCKLES WITH CHEESE GRATER
WELL DONE!! YOU HAVE NOW FAKED A FULL SET OF NINTENDO WII INJURIES. BASK IN THE ADMIRATION OF YOUR FRIENDS!
WII?
WII.
WOAH.
AndyRiley

Roasted
TRUE FACT:
IF YOU ZOOM IN ON YOUR OWN HOUSE ON GOOGLE EARTH, THEN LOOK UP, YOU'LL SEE YOUR OWN FACE LOOKING DOWN FROM THE SKY AND IT'S TEN MILES WIDE

Roasted
KARL, HAVE YOU SEEN THE —
OUT OF OFFICE AUTOREPLY: KARL'S MIND IS AWAY FROM WORK. KARL'S MIND WILL RESPOND WHEN IT RETURNS ON WEDNESDAY.

YEAH, IT'S JUST THIS SHOULD HAVE GOT SORTED BEFORE CHRISTMAS AND —
OUT OF OFFICE AUTOREPLY: KARL'S MIND IS AWAY FROM WORK. KARL'S MIND WILL RESPOND WHEN IT RETURNS ON WEDNESDAY.

KARL —
OUT OF OFFICE AUTOREPLY....
Andy Riley

Roasted
thought:
WHEN THE ARMY PUT DOWN THEIR CAMOUFLAGE GEAR FOR A SECOND -
HOW DO THEY FIND IT AGAIN?
Andy Riley

Roasted
the hardest question in a pub quiz is always:
So what are we going to call the team then?
"GREENLAND ICE SHEET."
"DONE A RUNNER"
"MINE'S A CIDER"
"GAY DALEK"
UMM....
"LOTTIE'S LEGENDS."
"KARL'S CREW."
"THE FLYING IANNUCCI BROTHERS."
"CRISPY DUCK."
"DOOMSDAY CLOCK SNOOZE FUNCTION"
"LILY ALLEN'S BLOODY DOG"
"BOULEVARD OF BROKEN DREAMS!"
"THE FANTASTIC THREE."
"ACTUAL BODILY HARM."
"SLICE OF FRIED GOLD."
"KWISATZ HADERACH."
"THE KAISER CHEATS!"
"THE SHITE STRIPES!"
"THE THIRD ATTENBOROUGH BROTHER."
"THIS IS DAVINA."
UMM....
"MICHAEL OWEN'S KNEE."
"THE TEAM WITH NO NAME."
Andy Riley

Roasted

THE SEARCH FOR TRUTH RESULTS IN:

TOO MUCH F████ TRUTH

Andy Riley

① CUT OUT THE RECTANGLE OF PAPER BELOW, AND KEEP IN YOUR WALLET OR PURSE. LAMINATE IT OR MOUNT IT ON CARD IF POSSIBLE.
NO IT ISN'T, OBVIOUSLY

② PRESENT IT TO THE NEXT PERSON YOU MEET WHO USES THE PHRASE "IT'S ALL GOOD."

WE ARE A PROUD NATION. WE SURVIVED "GET A LIFE." WE ENDURED "DON'T GO THERE."
TOGETHER WE CAN BEAT "IT'S ALL GOOD."
Andy Riley

Roasted
I OFFSET MY CARBON GUILT BY BUYING MORE PENCILS CAUSE THE GRAPHITE IS A LITTLE CARBON TRAP
Andy Riley

I OFFSET MY CARBON GUILT BY GIVING MY STAFF LESS DAYS OFF SO THEY DON'T FLY AWAY ON HOLIDAY

I OFFSET MY CARBON GUILT BY ALWAYS SAYING "IT DOESN'T MATTER WHAT WE DO CAUSE CHINA'S ON THE UP" WHENEVER THE SUBJECT ARISES

INSERT YOUR COMFORTING DELUSION HERE
I OFFSET MY CARBON GUILT BY ___
[YOU]

I'M LATE BECAUSE OF LONG-TERM UNDERFUNDING IN BRITAIN'S TRANSPORT INFRASTRUCTURE
THE SHORT-SIGHTED BEECHING REPORT AND THE ATROPHY OF THE BUS SERVICES HAVE COMBINED TO CREATE A LACK OF A VIABLE ALTERNATIVE FOR ME TO USE INSTEAD OF THE OVERLOADED ROAD NETWORK
WELL, IT WAS WORTH A GO
Andy Riley

Roasted

you know you're getting older when

Comic Relief seems to come round ***every six months***

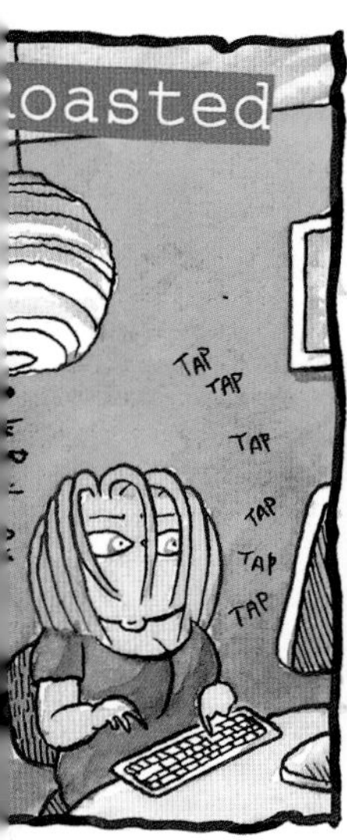
oasted
TAP
TAP
TAP
TAP
TAP
TAP

just sent u an email

IT'S KARL, LEAVE A MESSAGE.
HI, JUST RINGING TO SEE IF YOU GOT MY TEXT ABOUT THE E-MAIL

Karl
just a quick email
to see if you got
the answerphone
message about the text
about the email

hi text me if u got the email i sent about the answerphone message about the text about the email

etc.

IT'S CALLED A REMOTE

BECAUSE SOMEHOW IT'S ALWAYS TOO FAR AWAY